The approved documents

What is an approved document?

The Secretary of State has approved a series of documents that give practical guidance about how to meet the requirements of the Building Regulations 2010 for England. Approved documents give guidance on each of the technical parts of the regulations and on regulation 7 (see the back of this document).

Approved documents set out what, in ordinary circumstances, may be accepted as reasonable provision for compliance with the relevant requirements of the Building Regulations to which they refer. If you follow the guidance in an approved document, there will be a presumption of compliance with the requirements covered by the guidance. However, compliance is not guaranteed; for example, 'normal' guidance may not apply if the particular case is unusual in some way.

Note that there may be other ways to comply with the requirements – *there is no obligation to adopt any particular solution contained in an approved document*. If you prefer to meet a relevant requirement in some other way than described in an approved document, you should discuss this with the relevant building control body.

In addition to guidance, some approved documents include provisions that must be followed exactly, as required by regulations or where methods of test or calculation have been prescribed by the Secretary of State.

This approved document relates only to the particular requirements of the Building Regulations that the document addresses. However, building work must also comply with any other applicable requirements of the Building Regulations.

How to use this approved document

Each document uses the following conventions.

a. Text against a green background is an extract from the Building Regulations 2010 or the Building (Approved Inspectors etc.) Regulations 2010 (both as amended). These extracts set out the legal requirements of the regulations.

b. Key terms, printed in green, are defined in Appendix A.

c. When this approved document refers to a named standard or other document, the relevant version is listed in Appendix B (standards). However, if the issuing body has revised or updated the listed version of the standard or document, you may use the new version as guidance if it continues to address the relevant requirements of the Building Regulations.

NOTE: Standards and technical approvals may also address aspects of performance or matters that are not covered by the Building Regulations, or they may recommend higher standards than required by the Building Regulations.

Where you can get further help

If you do not understand the technical guidance or other information in this approved document or the additional detailed technical references to which it directs you, you can seek further help through a number of routes, some of which are listed below.

a. The Planning Portal website: www.planningportal.gov.uk.

b. *If you are the person undertaking the building work:* either from your local authority building control service or from an approved inspector.

c. *If you are registered with a competent person scheme:* from the scheme operator.

d. *If your query is highly technical:* from a specialist or an industry technical body for the relevant subject.

The Building Regulations

The following is a high level summary of the Building Regulations relevant to most types of building work. Where there is any doubt you should consult the full text of the regulations, available at www.legislation.gov.uk.

Building work

Regulation 3 of the Building Regulations defines 'building work'. Building work includes:

a. the erection or extension of a building

b. the provision or extension of a controlled service or fitting

c. the material alteration of a building or a controlled service or fitting.

Regulation 4 states that building work should be carried out in such a way that, when work is complete:

a. for new buildings or work on a building that complied with the applicable requirements of the Building Regulations: the building complies with the applicable requirements of the Building Regulations

b. for work on an existing building that did not comply with the applicable requirements of the Building Regulations:

   (i)   the work itself must comply with the applicable requirements of the Building Regulations

   (ii) the building must be no more unsatisfactory in relation to the requirements than before the work was carried out.

Material change of use

Regulation 5 defines a 'material change of use' in which a building or part of a building that was previously used for one purpose will be used for another.

The Building Regulations set out requirements that must be met before a building can be used for a new purpose. To meet the requirements, the building may need to be upgraded in some way.

Materials and workmanship

In accordance with regulation 7, building work must be carried out in a workmanlike manner using adequate and proper materials. Guidance on materials and workmanship is given in Approved Document 7.

Energy efficiency requirements

Part 6 of the Building Regulations imposes additional specific requirements for energy efficiency.

If a building is extended or renovated, the energy efficiency of the existing building or part of it may need to be upgraded.

Notification of work

Most building work and material changes of use must be notified to a building control body unless one of the following applies.

a. It is work that will be self-certified by a registered competent person or certified by a registered third party.

b. It is work exempted from the need to notify by regulation 12(6A) of, or Schedule 4 to, the Building Regulations.

Responsibility for compliance

People who are responsible for building work (e.g. agent, designer, builder or installer) must ensure that the work complies with all applicable requirements of the Building Regulations. The building owner may also be responsible for ensuring that work complies with the Building Regulations. If building work does not comply with the Building Regulations, the building owner may be served with an enforcement notice.

Contents

Approved Document K: Protection from falling, collision and impact

Summary

0.1 This approved document gives guidance on how to comply with Parts K1, K2, K3, K4, K5.1, K5.2, K5.3, K5.4 and K6 of the Building Regulations. It contains the following sections:

Section 1:	Guidance on aspects of the geometry of stairs, special stairs, fixed ladders and handrails for and guarding of stairs
Section 2:	Guidance on ramps and guarding of ramps
Section 3:	Guidance on protection from falling
Section 4:	Guidance on vehicle barriers and loading bays
Section 5:	Guidance on protection against impact with glazing
Section 6:	Guidance on protection from collision with open windows etc.
Section 7:	Guidance on manifestation of glazing
Section 8:	Guidance on safe opening and closing of windows etc.
Section 9:	Guidance on safe access for cleaning windows etc.
Section 10:	Guidance on protection against impact from and trapping by doors.

Application

0.2 Regulation 3 defines building work such that the following applies.

    a. Glazing which is installed in a location where there was none previously as part of the erection, extension or material alteration of a building (other than an exempt building), and the replacement of a whole unit (i.e. the frame and glazing) is building work and is subject to requirement K4 and K5.2.

    b. The replacement of glazing whilst retaining an existing frame (e.g. as a repair) is not building work, but the supply of the glazing may be subject to consumer protection legislation.

0.3 Requirement K1 applies to means of access outside a building only when the access is part of the building (i.e. attached). For example, requirement K1 does not apply to steps on land leading to a building, but does apply to entrance steps which are part of the building.

0.4 Regarding access routes.

    a. Where access and circulation routes form part of a means of escape for people in case of fire, refer to Approved Document B: Fire safety, Volume 1 – Dwellinghouses, and Volume 2 – Buildings other than dwellinghouses.

    b. For external pedestrian access and circulation routes to buildings, from the boundary of the site and car parking, reference should also be made to Approved Document M: Access to and use of buildings.

Interaction with other legislation

0.6 The guidance provided in this document is in relation to the permanent features which form part of the building providing reasonable safety in the appropriate circumstances. However, there may well be particular situations, such as access for maintenance required less frequently than once a month (e.g. see paragraph 1.42b), where such permanent features may be less appropriate. Where this may be the case the Construction (Design and Management) Regulations 2007 provides detail on procedures for safe use of temporary means of access, together with focus on effective planning and management of risk.

0.7 Health and safety regulations such as the Workplace (Health, Safety and Welfare) Regulations 1992 may impose requirements on employers and those in control of premises used as workplaces in relation to certain physical characteristics of the workplace. Where such regulations apply there may be confusion as to whether the Building Regulations or health and safety requirements take precedence, as both will apply. Where an inspector for the purposes of the Health and Safety at Work, etc. Act 1974 has identified a contravention of such health and safety regulations they may seek to serve an improvement notice to secure compliance. In such circumstances the inspector is prevented by virtue of section 23(3) of the Health and Safety at Work, etc. Act 1974 from requiring measures which are more onerous than necessary to comply with any requirements of the Building Regulations, unless the specific requirement of health and safety regulations are themselves more onerous. Where applicable the following cross-referencing should be made.

a. For building work relating to requirement K1 of the Building Regulations, regarding the design of stairs, ladders and ramps, see regulation 17 of the Workplace (Health, Safety and Welfare) Regulations 1992. Regulation 17 relates to permanent stairs, ladders and ramps on pedestrian routes within the workplace premises, including those used to give access for maintenance to parts of the workplace premises.

b. For building work relating to requirement K2 of the Building Regulations, regarding the avoidance of risk from falling when working at height, see regulation 6 of the Work at Height Regulations 2005.

c. For building work relating to requirement K3 of the Building Regulations, regarding the design of vehicle barriers and loading bays, see regulation 17 of the Workplace (Health, Safety and Welfare) Regulations 1992.

d. For building work relating to requirement K4 of the Building Regulations, regarding the prevention of personal injury, see regulation 14(1)(a) of the Workplace (Health, Safety and Welfare) Regulations 1992.

e. For building work relating to requirement K5.1 of the Building Regulations, regarding the requirements for projecting windows, skylights and ventilators, see regulation 15(2) of the Workplace (Health, Safety and Welfare) Regulations 1992.

f. For building work relating to requirement K5.2 of the Building Regulations, regarding the requirements for marking windows, transparent or translucent doors, gates and walls, see regulation 14(1)(b) of the Workplace (Health, Safety and Welfare) Regulations 1992.

g. For building work relating to requirement K5.3 of the Building Regulations, regarding the requirements for opening, closing or adjusting windows, skylights and ventilators, see regulation 15(1) of the Workplace (Health, Safety and Welfare) Regulations 1992.

h. For building work relating to requirement K5.4 of the Building Regulations, regarding the requirements for cleaning windows and skylights, etc., see regulation 16 of the Workplace (Health, Safety and Welfare) Regulations 1992.

i. For building work relating to requirement K6 of the Building Regulations, regarding the requirements for doors and gates, see regulation 18 of the Workplace (Health, Safety and Welfare) Regulations 1992.

Requirement K1: Stairs, ladders and ramps

This approved document deals with the following requirement from Part K of Schedule 1 to the Building Regulations 2010.

Requirements	
Requirement	*Limits on application*
Stairs, ladders and ramps	
K1. Stairs, ladders and ramps shall be so designed, constructed and installed as to be safe for people moving between different levels in or about the building.	Requirement K1 applies only to stairs, ladders and ramps which form part of the building.

Performance

In the Secretary of State's view, you can meet requirement K1 by ensuring that the steepness, rise and going, handrails, headroom, length and width of any stairs, ladders and ramps between levels are appropriate to afford reasonable safety to people gaining access to and moving about buildings.

The standard of provision needed to give an acceptable level of safety for access and use depends on the circumstances.

a. The standard of provision may need to be higher in a public building than in a dwelling, because people may not be familiar with the building and there may be more users.

b. A lower standard of provision may be acceptable where access is required only for maintenance, because greater care can be expected from the people requiring to gain access.

Section 1: Stairs and ladders

Scope

1.1 The guidance provided in this document covers internal and external steps and stairs when they are part of the building. Additional guidance is provided in Approved Document M when external stepped access also forms part of the principal entrances and alternative accessible entrances, and when they form part of the access route to the building from the boundary of the site and car parking. See Approved Document M Section 1 (for buildings other than dwellings) and Section 6 (for dwellings).

Steepness of stairs – rise and going

1.2 Measure the rise and going as shown in Diagram 1.1. (For steps with tapered treads, see also paragraphs 1.25–1.27.)

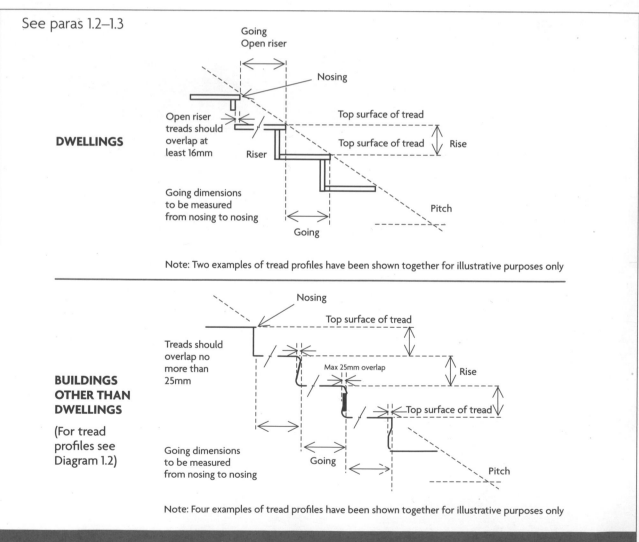

Diagram 1.1   Measuring rise and going

1.3 In a flight of steps, for all steps use the measurements for rise and going given for the three stair categories in Table 1.1 below. Use any rise between the minimum and maximum with any going between the minimum and maximum, that complies with the relevant note contained in table 1.1.

Table 1.1 Rise and going

	Rise*		Going*	
	Minimum (mm)	Maximum (mm)	Minimum (mm)	Maximum (mm)
Private stair[1, 2]	150	220	220	300
Utility stair	150	190	250	400
General access stair[3]	150	170	250	400

Notes:

[1] The maximum pitch for a private stair is 42°.

[2] For dwellings, for external tapered steps and stairs that are part of the building the going of each step should be a minimum of 280mm.

[3] For school buildings, the preferred going is 280mm and rise is 150mm.

* The normal relationship between the dimensions of the rise and going is: twice the rise plus the going (2R + G) equals between 550mm and 700mm.

For existing buildings the dimensional requirements in Table 1.1 should be followed, unless due to dimensional constraints it is not possible. Any alternative proposal should be agreed with the relevant building control body and included in an access strategy (refer to Approved Document M).

Stepped gangways in assembly buildings

1.4 The guidance provided in this document covers stairs or ramps that form part of the means of access within an assembly building such as a sports stadium, theatre or cinema. However, if steps are part of the gangways to areas for spectators, the gangways may need to be at different pitches to maintain sightlines for spectators – this may affect the main stairs. Apply all of the following guidance.

a. Ensure that the maximum pitch for gangways to seating areas for spectators is 35°.

b. Align the ends of all rows of seats/wheelchair spaces so that the width of the gangway remains the same.

c. Provide transverse gangways to give access from the side to storey exits (vomitory exits) within the body of a seating layout.

d. Ensure that transverse gangways and radial gangways in auditoria with tiered seating do not cross. Offset the connections between transverse gangways and radial gangways so that the flow of people to the exits is smooth.

e. In stepped tiers, use the following measurements for each step in the gangway:

　(i) minimum height: 100mm

　(ii) maximum height: 190mm

　If there are two or more rises to each row of seats, make each step an equal height.

f In a tier that is uninterrupted by cross-gangways, and where the pitch exceeds 25°, use a maximum number of steps of 40.

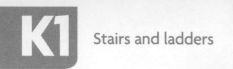

g. Where an exit is approached from a stepped gangway, place a landing the width of the exit and a minimum of 1100mm deep immediately in front of the exit doors.

h. For stepped side gangways, provide a handrail in accordance with paragraphs 1.34 and 1.36.

i. In stepped tiers, maintain the same level between the seatway and the nearest step.

j. Gangways should not be less than 1100mm wide unless used by not more than 50 persons, in which case gangways should be a minimum of 900mm.

Construction of steps

For all buildings

1.5 Have level treads on steps, ensuring that the rise and going of each step are consistent throughout a flight of steps and are in accordance with Table 1.1.

For buildings other than dwellings

1.6 Use risers that are not open.

NOTE: The benefits of a riser that is not open are as follows.

a. It removes the possibility of the front of a foot or a walking aid being caught underneath a tread during ascent, possibly causing a fall.

b. It avoids the feeling of insecurity people get when looking through open risers on a stair.

1.7 For steps, apply both of the following guidance.

a. Make step nosings apparent: use a material that will contrast visually, a minimum of 55mm wide, on both the tread and the riser.

b. Avoid, if possible, step nosings that protrude over the tread below. If the nosing protrudes, ensure that this is by no more than 25mm (see Diagram 1.2).

1.8 If the soffit beneath a stair is less than 2m above floor level, protect the area beneath a stair with one of the following.

a. Guarding and low level cane detection.

b. A barrier giving the same degree of protection.

For dwellings

1.9 Steps may have open risers if they comply with both of the following guidance.

a. Overlap treads by a minimum of 16mm.

b. Construct the steps so that a 100mm diameter sphere cannot pass through the open risers.

For common access areas in buildings that contain flats

1.10 Provide a stair with steps that comply with all of the following guidance.

a. Make step nosings apparent: use a material that will contrast visually, 50mm to 65mm wide on the tread and 30mm to 55mm on the riser.

b. Use a suitable tread nosing profile, as shown in Diagram 1.2.

c. Use risers which are not open.

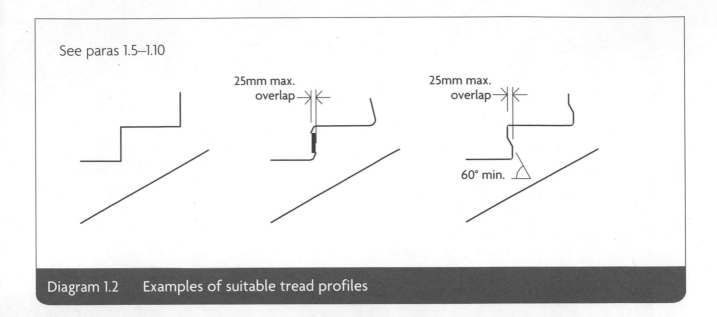

Diagram 1.2   Examples of suitable tread profiles

Headroom for stairs

For all buildings

1.11 On the access between levels, provide the minimum headroom shown in Diagram 1.3.

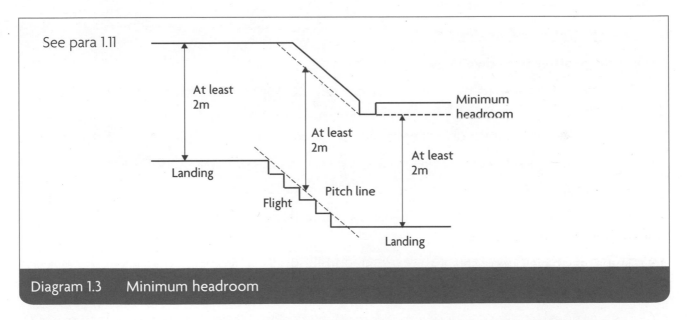

Diagram 1.3   Minimum headroom

For buildings other than dwellings and common access areas in buildings that contain flats

1.12 Provide all means of escape routes with a minimum clear headroom of 2m, except in doorways.

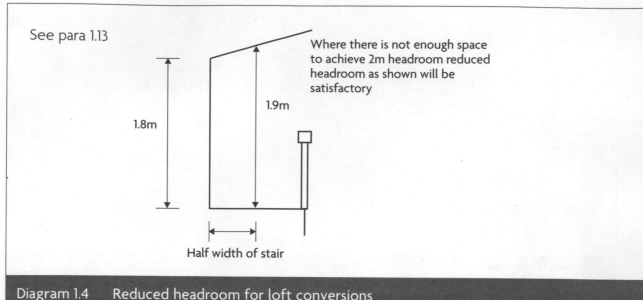

See para 1.13

1.8m

1.9m

Where there is not enough space to achieve 2m headroom reduced headroom as shown will be satisfactory

Half width of stair

Diagram 1.4   Reduced headroom for loft conversions

For loft conversions in dwellings

1.13 Where there is not enough space to achieve the height shown in Diagram 1.3, provide the reduced headroom shown in Diagram 1.4.

Width of flights of stairs

For buildings other than dwellings

1.14 For stairs that form part of means of escape, refer to Approved Document B: Fire safety, Volume 2 – Buildings other than dwellinghouses.

1.15 For flights of stairs which do not form part of the means of escape, provide all of the following.

a. A minimum stair width between enclosing walls, strings or upstands of 1200mm.

b. A minimum width between handrails of 1000mm.

c. If the flight is more than 2m wide, divide it into flights a minimum of 1000mm wide, as shown in Diagram 1.5

d. For access for maintenance, see paragraph 1.42.

For dwellings

1.16 In exceptional circumstances where severely sloping plots are involved, a stepped change of level within the entrance storey may be unavoidable. In those instances ensure that stairs within the entrance storey of a dwelling have flights with a minimum stair width of 900mm.

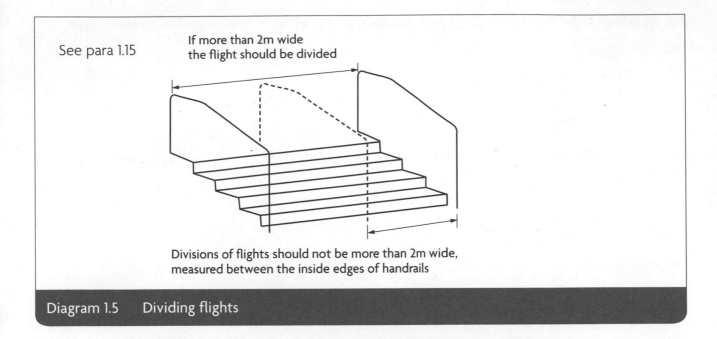

Diagram 1.5   Dividing flights

Length of flights of stairs

For all buildings

1.17 If stairs have more than 36 risers in consecutive flights, make a minimum of one change of direction between flights, as shown in Diagram 1.6.

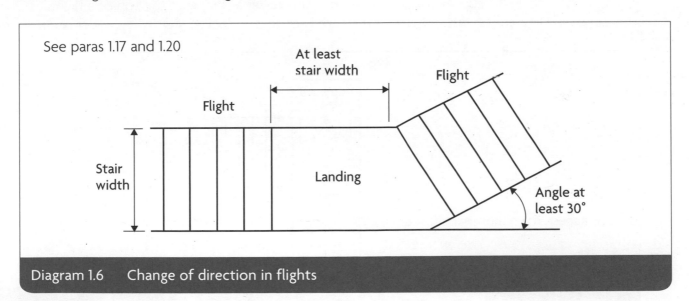

Diagram 1.6   Change of direction in flights

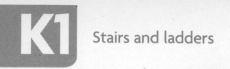
For buildings other than dwellings and common access areas in buildings that contain flats

1.18 Comply with all of the following.

    a. Do not have single steps.

    b. For flights between landings the maximum number of risers should be:

        (i)   utility stairs – 16 risers

        (ii)   general access stairs – 12 risers, but exceptionally no more than 16 in small premises where the plan area is restricted

        (iii) stairs for access for maintenance, see paragraph 1.42.

Landings for stairs

For all buildings

1.19 For means of escape requirements, refer to Approved Document B: Volume 1 – Dwellinghouses, and Volume 2 – Buildings other than dwellinghouses.

1.20 At the top and bottom of every flight, provide landings the width and length at least as great as the smallest width of the flight (see Diagram 1.6).

1.21 A landing:

    a. may include part of the floor of the building

    b. should be kept clear of permanent obstructions

    c. may have doors to cupboards and ducts that open over a landing at the top of a flight, as shown in Diagram 1.7, but only when they are kept shut or locked shut when under normal use.

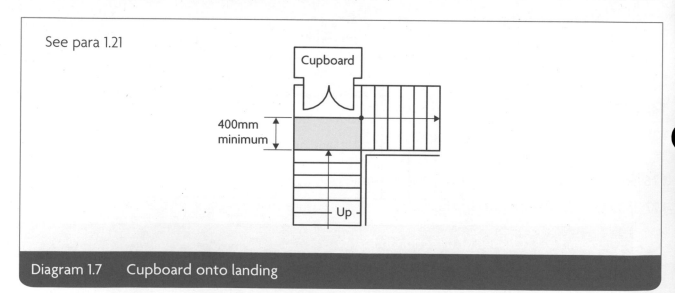

See para 1.21

400mm minimum

Cupboard

Up

Diagram 1.7   Cupboard onto landing

1.22 Landings should be level, *with the following exception.*

A landing at the top or bottom of a flight that is formed by the ground may have a gradient, provided that:

    a. the maximum gradient along the direction of travel is 1:60

    b. the surface is paved ground or otherwise made permanently firm.

For buildings other than dwellings

1.23 Provide all of the following.

    a. An unobstructed length a minimum of 1200mm on each landing.

    b. Doors that do not swing across landings, except where they comply with paragraph 1.21c.

    c. For access for maintenance, see paragraph 1.42.

For dwellings

1.24 A door may swing across a landing at the bottom of a flight, but only as shown in Diagram 1.8.

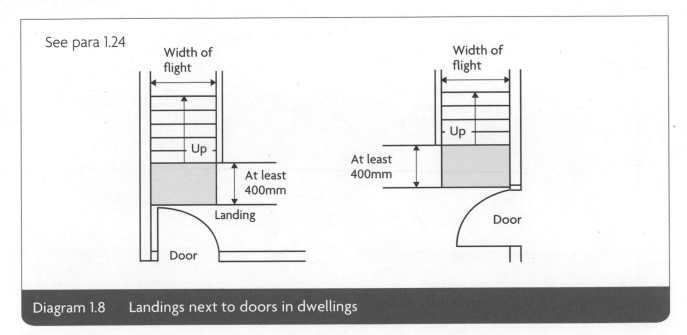

| Diagram 1.8 | Landings next to doors in dwellings |

Special stairs

Tapered treads

1.25 For the rise and going, comply with paragraphs 1.2 and 1.3. For the going of tapered treads, use the measurements shown in Diagram 1.9.

1.26 For consecutive tapered treads, use the same going.

1.27 If a stair consists of straight and tapered treads, ensure that the going of the tapered treads is not less than the going of the straight treads.

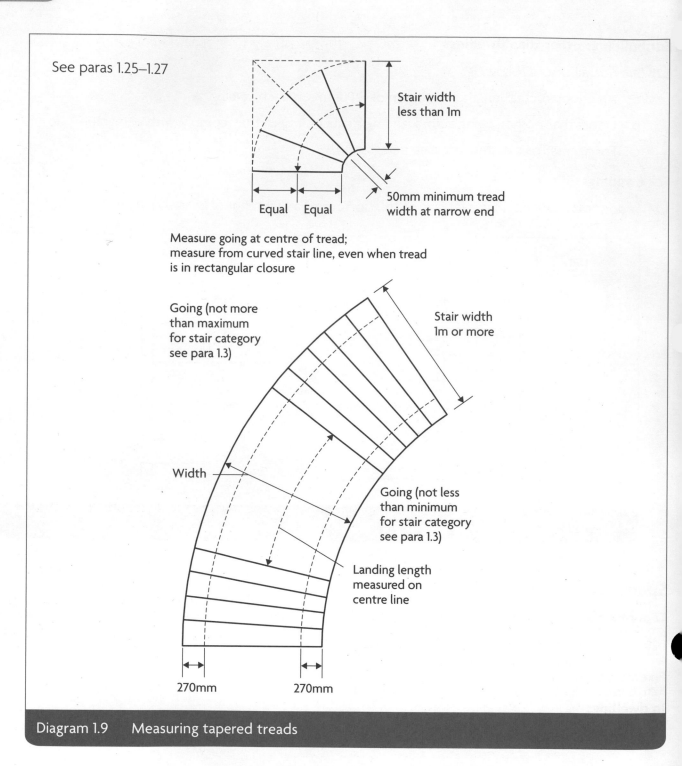

See paras 1.25–1.27

Stair width less than 1m

50mm minimum tread width at narrow end

Equal   Equal

Measure going at centre of tread; measure from curved stair line, even when tread is in rectangular closure

Going (not more than maximum for stair category see para 1.3)

Stair width 1m or more

Width

Going (not less than minimum for stair category see para 1.3)

Landing length measured on centre line

270mm   270mm

Diagram 1.9   Measuring tapered treads

Spiral and helical stairs

1.28 Design spiral stairs and helical stairs in accordance with **BS 5395-2**.

Alternating tread stairs in dwellings

1.29 You may use alternating tread stairs – in one or more straight flights – only in a loft conversion, and only when there is not enough space for a stair that satisfies paragraphs 1.2–1.24, and the stair is for access to only one habitable room and, if desired, a bathroom and/or a WC (although this must not be the only WC in the dwelling).

1.30 The construction of an alternating tread stair should comply with all of the following.

a. Comply with Diagram 1.10.

b. Make alternating steps uniform with parallel nosings.

c. Have slip-resistant surfaces on treads.

d. Ensure that the tread sizes over the wider part of the step are in line with the dimensions in Table 1.1.

e. Comply with paragraph 1.9b.

f. Provide a minimum clear headroom of 2m.

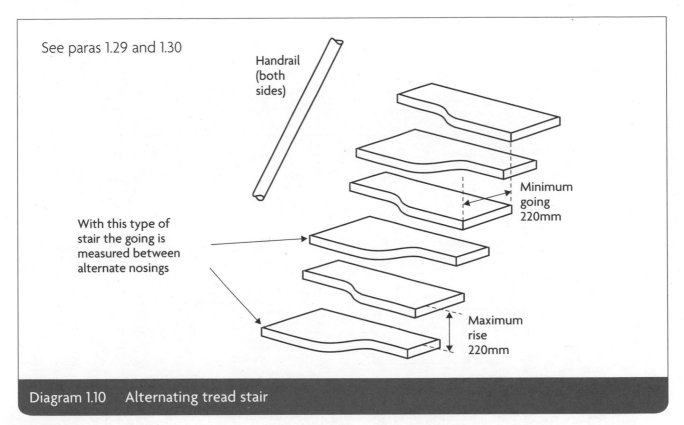

See paras 1.29 and 1.30

Handrail (both sides)

With this type of stair the going is measured between alternate nosings

Minimum going 220mm

Maximum rise 220mm

Diagram 1.10   Alternating tread stair

Fixed ladders

In dwellings

1.31 Do not use retractable ladders as means of escape. Refer to Approved Document B: Volume 1 – Dwellinghouses, and Volume 2 – Buildings other than dwellinghouses.

1.32 You may use a fixed ladder – with fixed handrails on both sides – only for access in a loft conversion that contains one habitable room, and only when there is not enough space without alteration to the existing space for a stair that satisfies the guidance for dwellings in paragraphs 1.2–1.24.

For industrial buildings

1.33 Design and construct stairs, ladders and walkways, as appropriate, in accordance with **BS 5395-3** or **BS 4211**.

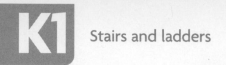

Handrails for stairs

For all buildings

1.34 Provide handrails in accordance with all of the following.

  a. Position the top of the handrail 900mm to 1100mm from the pitch line or floor.

  b. The handrail may form the top of a guarding if you can match the heights.

  c. If the stairs are 1000mm or wider: provide a handrail on both sides.

For buildings other than dwellings and common access areas in buildings that contain flats and do not have passenger lifts

1.35 Provide suitable continuous handrails, as dimensioned in Diagram 1.11 (for blocks of flats) and Diagram 1.12 (for buildings other than dwellings), in accordance with both of the following.

  a. On each side of the flights.

  b. On each side of the landings.

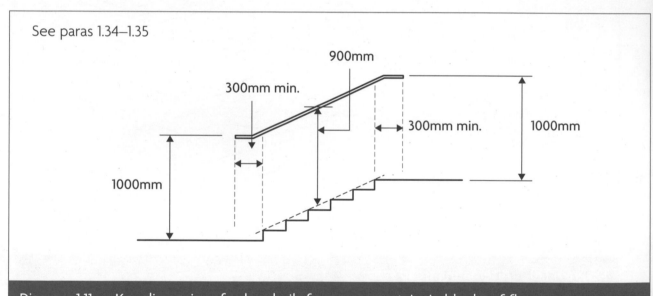

See paras 1.34–1.35

Diagram 1.11   Key dimensions for handrails for common stairs in blocks of flats

For buildings other than dwellings

1.36 Provide handrails in accordance with all of the following (in addition to paragraph 1.34).

  a. Where there is full-height structural guarding, if you provide a second (lower) handrail, the vertical height from the pitch line of the steps (or the surface of the ramp) to the top of the second (lower) handrail should be 600mm.

  b. Use a continuous handrail along the flights and landings of a ramped or stepped flight.

  c. Ensure that handrails do not project into an access route.

  d. Ensure that the handrail will contrast visually with the background against which it is seen, without being highly reflective.

e.   Use a surface for the handrail that is slip-resistant and which, in locations subject to extremely cold or hot temperatures, does not become excessively cold or hot to touch. In areas where resistance to vandalism or low maintenance are key factors, use of metals with relatively low thermal conductivity may be appropriate.

f.   Finish the end of the handrail in a way that reduces the risk of clothing being caught.

g.   Use the handrail profile shown in Diagram 1.13.

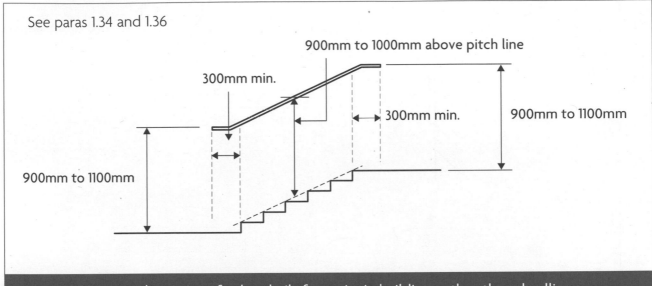

See paras 1.34 and 1.36

900mm to 1000mm above pitch line

300mm min.

300mm min.

900mm to 1100mm

900mm to 1100mm

Diagram 1.12   Key dimensions for handrails for stairs in buildings other than dwellings

In dwellings

1.37 In exceptional circumstances where severely sloping plots are involved, a stepped change of level within the entrance storey may be unavoidable. In those instances, if a flight comprises three or more risers, provide a suitable continuous handrail in accordance with both of the following.

a.   On each side of the flight.

b.   On each side of any intermediate landings.

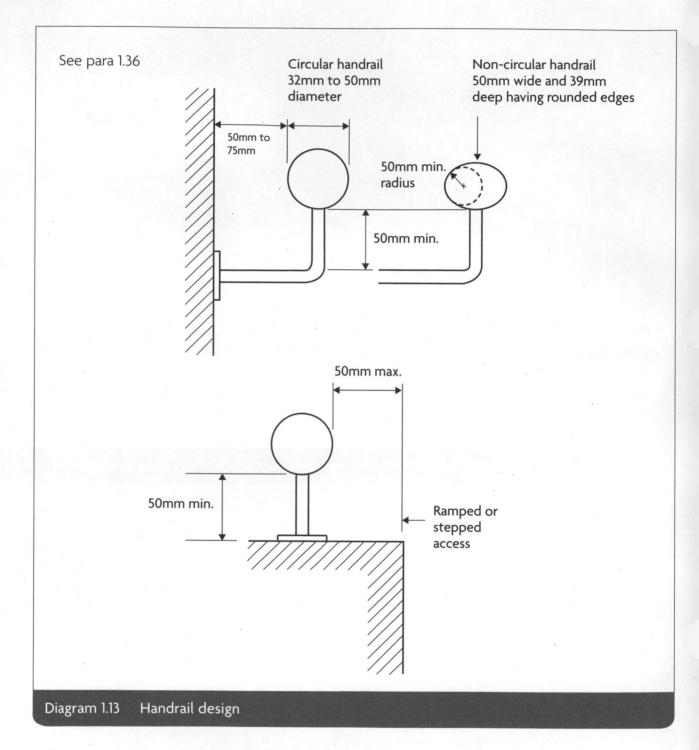

See para 1.36

Circular handrail
32mm to 50mm
diameter

Non-circular handrail
50mm wide and 39mm
deep having rounded edges

50mm to
75mm

50mm min.
radius

50mm min.

50mm max.

50mm min.

Ramped or
stepped
access

Diagram 1.13   Handrail design

Guarding of stairs

For all buildings

1.38 Design the guarding to be the height shown in Diagram 3.1.

1.39 In a building that may be used by children under five years of age, construct the guarding to a flight of stairs to do both of the following.

a. Prevent children being held fast by the guarding: ensure that a 100mm sphere cannot pass through any openings in the guarding.

b. Prevent children from readily being able to climb the guarding.

For buildings other than dwellings and common access areas for buildings that contain flats

1.40 Provide guarding at the sides of flights and landings when there are two or more risers.

In dwellings

1.41 Provide guarding at the sides of flights and landings when there is a drop of more than 600mm.

Access for maintenance

For buildings other than dwellings

1.42 Where the stairs or ladders will be used to access areas for maintenance they should comply with one of the following.

    a. If access will be required a minimum of once per month: follow provisions such as those for private stairs in dwellings or for industrial stairs and ladders in **BS 5395-3**.

    b. If access will be required less frequently than once a month: it may be appropriate, for example, to use portable ladders. The Construction (Design and Management) Regulations 2007 give provisions for safe use of temporary means of access.

Section 2: Ramps

Scope

2.1 The guidance provided in this document covers internal and external ramps when they are part of the building. Additional guidance is provided in Approved Document M when external ramped access also forms part of the principal entrances and alternative accessible entrances, and when they form part of the access route to the building from the boundary of the site and car parking. See Approved Document M Section 1 (for buildings other than dwellings) and Section 6 (for dwellings).

Appearance of ramps

For buildings other than dwellings

2.2 Ensure that ramps are readily apparent or clearly signposted.

Steepness of ramps

For all buildings

2.3 Ensure that the relationship between the gradient of a ramp and its going between landings is as shown in Diagram 2.1.

> **NOTE:** A floor level with a gradient of 1:20 or steeper should be designed as a ramp.

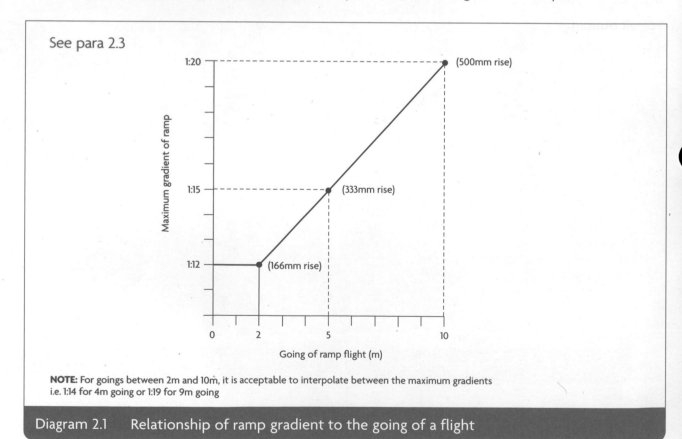

See para 2.3

NOTE: For goings between 2m and 10m, it is acceptable to interpolate between the maximum gradients i.e. 1:14 for 4m going or 1:19 for 9m going

Diagram 2.1   Relationship of ramp gradient to the going of a flight

Construction of ramps

For buildings other than dwellings

2.4 A ramps surface should be selected in accordance with both of the following.

a. Use a ramp surface that is slip resistant, especially when wet, and a colour that will contrast visually with that of the landings.

b. Ensure that the frictional characteristics of the ramp and landing surfaces are similar.

2.5 On the open side of any ramp or landing, in addition to any guarding, provide a kerb that complies with both of the following.

a. Is a minimum of 100mm high.

b. Will contrast visually with the ramp or landing.

2.6 Where the change of level is:

a. 300mm or more: in addition to the ramp, provide two or more clearly signposted steps

b. less than 300mm: provide a ramp instead of a single step.

2.7 If the soffit beneath any ramp is less than 2m above floor level, protect the area beneath the ramp with one of the following.

a. Guarding and low level cane detection.

b. A barrier giving the same degree of protection.

Design of ramps

For all buildings

2.8 Design all ramps and landings in accordance with Diagram 2.2.

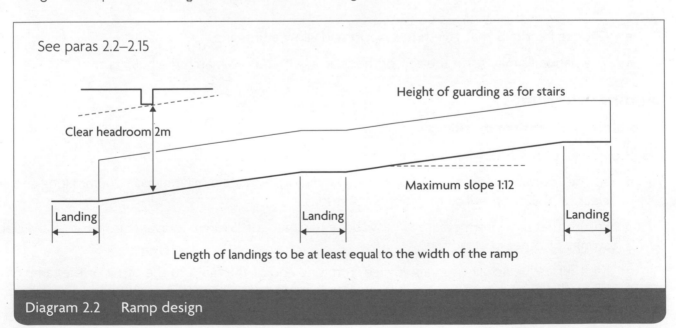

See paras 2.2–2.15

Clear headroom 2m

Height of guarding as for stairs

Maximum slope 1:12

Landing   Landing   Landing

Length of landings to be at least equal to the width of the ramp

Diagram 2.2   Ramp design

Width of ramps

For buildings other than dwellings

2.9 Regarding the width of a ramp.

    a. For a ramp that provides access for people: ensure the ramp has a minimum width between walls, upstands or kerbs of 1500mm.

    b. For a ramp that forms a means of escape: see Approved Document B: Volume 2 – Buildings other than dwellinghouses, B1, Section 5.

Obstruction of ramps

For all buildings

2.10 Keep ramps clear of permanent obstructions.

Handrails for ramps

For buildings other than dwellings

2.11 Provide a handrail on both sides of the ramp and design them to comply with paragraph 1.36.

In dwellings and common access areas in buildings that contain flats

2.12 Provide all of the following.

    a. For ramps that are less than 1000mm wide: provide a handrail on one or both sides.

    b. For ramps that are 1000mm or more wide: provide a handrail on both sides.

    c. For ramps that are 600mm or less in height: you do not need to provide handrails.

    d. Position the top of the handrails at a height of 900mm to 1000mm above the surface of the ramp.

    e. Choose handrails that give firm support and allow a firm grip.

    f. The handrails may form the top of the guarding if you can match the heights.

Landings for ramps

For buildings other than dwellings

2.13 Provide all of the following.

    a. At the foot and head of a ramp, provide landings which are a minimum of 1200mm long and are clear of any door swings or other obstructions.

    b. Ensure that any intermediate landings are a minimum of 1500mm long and are clear of any door swings or other obstructions.

    c. If either a wheelchair user cannot see from one end of the ramp to the other or the ramp has three flights or more then provide intermediate landings a minimum of 1800mm wide and a minimum of 1800mm long as passing places.

    d. Make all landings level or with a maximum gradient of 1:60 along their length.

For dwellings and common access areas in buildings that contain flats

2.14 Provide landings for ramps, as described for stairs in paragraphs 1.19–1.22 and 1.24.

Guarding of ramps

For all buildings

2.15 Provide guarding for ramps and their landings at their sides in the same way as stairs (see paragraphs 1.38–1.41).

Requirement K2: Protection from falling

This approved document deals with the following requirement from Part K of Schedule 1 to the Building Regulations 2010.

Requirements	
Requirement	*Limits on application*
Protection from falling	
K2.—(a) Any stairs, ramps, floors and balconies and any roof to which people have access, and	Requirement K2 (a) applies only to stairs and ramps which form part of the building.
(b) any light well, basement area or similar sunken area connected to a building,	
shall be provided with barriers where it is necessary to protect people in or about the building from falling.	

Performance

In the Secretary of State's view, you can meet requirement K2 if, in order to reduce the risk to the safety of people in and around buildings, you use suitable guarding for the appropriate circumstance. Unless otherwise set out elsewhere in this document for particular situations, you can achieve this by the following:

a. in *dwellings:* provide pedestrian guarding that is capable of preventing people from being injured by falling from a height of more than 600mm

b. in *buildings other than dwellings:* provide pedestrian guarding that is capable of preventing people from falling more than the height of two risers (or 380mm, if not part of a stair).

The standard of provision for guarding needed to give an acceptable level of safety depends on the circumstances. For example, in a public building the standard of provision may need to be higher than in a dwelling, because people may be less familiar with the building and there may be more users.

For areas where access is required only for maintenance, greater care can be expected from people and therefore a lower standard of provision may be acceptable.

Section 3: Protection from falling

Siting of pedestrian guarding

For all buildings

3.1 Provide guarding in all of the following locations:

a. where it is reasonably necessary for safety to guard the edges of any part of a floor (including the edge below an opening window), gallery, balcony, roof (including roof lights and other openings), any other place to which people have access, and any light well, basement or similar sunken area next to a building

b. in vehicle parks.

NOTE: You do *not* need to provide guarding in the following locations:

a. on ramps used only for vehicle access

b. in places such as loading bays where it would obstruct normal use.

Design of guarding

For all buildings

3.2 Guarding should be provided in accordance with all of the following.

a. Ensure that guarding is, as a minimum, the height shown in Diagram 3.1.

b. You can use any wall, parapet, balustrade or similar obstruction as guarding.

c. Ensure that guarding can resist, as a minimum, the loads given in **BS EN 1991-1-1** with its UK National Annex and **PD 6688-1-1**.

d. Where glazing is used in the guarding, refer also to Section 5 in this approved document.

NOTE: Typical locations for guarding are shown in Diagram 3.2.

For further guidance on the design of barriers and infill panels, refer to **BS 6180**.

Building Category and location See paras 1.38, 3.2 and 3.4		Height (h)	
Single family dwellings	Stairs, landings, ramps, edges of internal floors	900mm for all elements	
	External balconies, including Juliette balconies and edges of roof	1100mm	
Factories and warehouses (light traffic)	Stairs, ramps	900mm	
	Landings and edges of floors	1100mm	
Residential, institutional, educational, office and public buildings	All locations	900mm for flights otherwise 1100mm	
Assembly	Within 530mm in front of fixed seating	800mm (h1)	
	All other locations	900mm for flights elsewhere 1100mm (h2)	
Retail	All locations	900mm for flights otherwise 1100mm	
Glazing in all buildings	At opening windows except roof windows in loft extensions, see Approved Document B1	800mm	
	At glazing to changes of levels to provide containment	Below 800mm	

Diagram 3.1   Guarding design

3.3   In a building that may be used by children under five years of age during normal use, guarding should be constructed in accordance with both of the following.

a.   To prevent children being held fast by the guarding: ensure that a 100mm sphere cannot pass through any openings in the guarding.

b.   To prevent children from readily being able to climb the guarding: avoid horizontal rails.

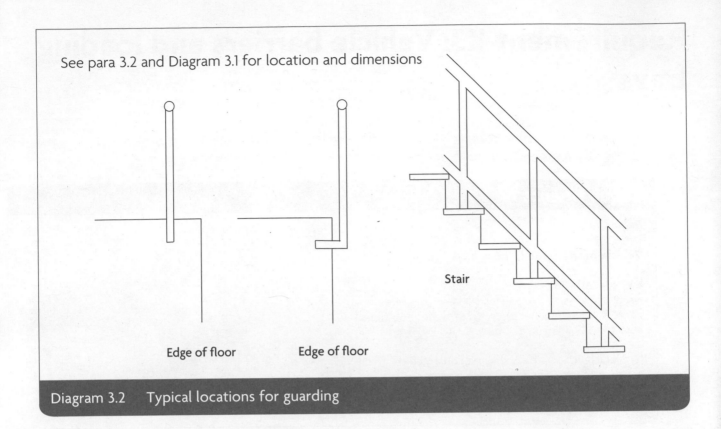

See para 3.2 and Diagram 3.1 for location and dimensions

Stair

Edge of floor   Edge of floor

Diagram 3.2   Typical locations for guarding

Guarding of areas used for maintenance

For all buildings

3.4 Where people will use the stairs or ladders to access areas for maintenance they should comply with one of the following.

   a. If access will be required frequently (e.g. a minimum of once per month): follow provisions such as those suggested for dwellings in this Approved Document (see Diagram 3.1).

   b. If access will be required less frequently than once a month: it may be appropriate to use temporary guarding or warning notices. The Construction (Design and Management) Regulations 2007 and the Work at Height Regulations 2005 give provisions for such measures.

3.5 Use signs as specified in the Health and Safety (Safety Signs and Signals) Regulations 1996.

Requirement K3: Vehicle barriers and loading bays

This approved document deals with the following requirement from Part K of Schedule 1 to the Building Regulations 2010.

Requirements

Requirement	Limits on application
Vehicle barriers and loading bays	
K3.—(1) Vehicle ramps and any levels in a building to which vehicles have access, shall be provided with barriers where it is necessary to protect people in or about the building.	
(2) Vehicle loading bays shall be constructed in such a way, or be provided with such features, as may be necessary to protect people in them from collision with vehicles.	

Performance

In the Secretary of State's view, you can meet requirement K3 if, in order to reduce the risk to the safety of people from collision with vehicles in and about buildings, you:

a. provide vehicle barriers that are capable of resisting or deflecting the impact of vehicles

b. provide loading bays that have an adequate number of exits or refuges which enable people to avoid being struck or crushed by vehicles.

The standard of provision for guarding needed to give an acceptable level of safety depends on the circumstances. For example, in a public building the standard of provision may need to be higher than in a dwelling, because people may be less familiar with the building and there may be more users.

For areas where access is required only for maintenance, greater care can be expected from people and therefore a lower standard of provision may be acceptable.

Section 4: Vehicle barriers and loading bays

Vehicle barriers

For all buildings

4.1 If vehicles have access to a floor, roof or ramp which forms part of a building, provide barriers at any edges which are level with or above the floor or ground or any other route for vehicles (see Diagram 4.1).

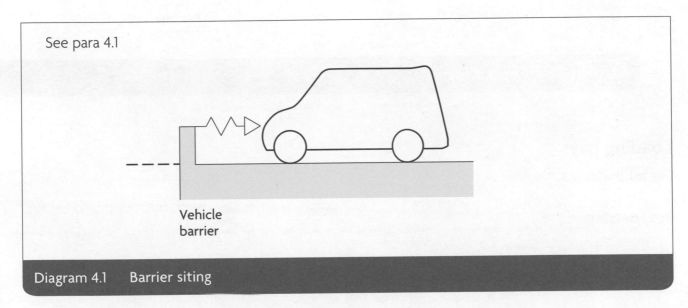

See para 4.1

Vehicle barrier

Diagram 4.1   Barrier siting

4.2 Barriers should be provided in accordance with all of the following.

a. You can use any wall, parapet, balustrade or similar obstacle as a barrier.

b. Construct barriers to be, as a minimum, the height shown in Diagram 4.2.

c. Ensure that barriers can resist the loads given in **BS EN 1991-1-1** with its UK National Annex and **PD 6688-1-1**.

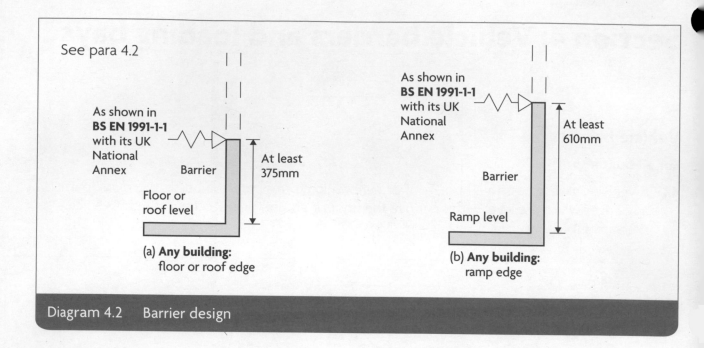

Diagram 4.2   Barrier design

Loading bays

For all buildings

4.3 Loading bays should be constructed with exit points in accordance with both of the following.

a. Provide loading bays with a minimum of one exit point from the lower level, as near the centre of the rear wall as possible.

b. For wide loading bays (for three or more vehicles), provide a minimum of two stepped exit points, one on each side, or provide a refuge where people can avoid the path of a vehicle in addition to one stepped exit point (see Diagram 4.3).

Guarding for loading bays

For all buildings

4.4 Where there is a danger of people falling, loading bays should be provided with guarding as per the guidance provided in this approved document. If guarding is not practical for the particular circumstances, alternative safeguards should be provided and agreed with the building control body.

See para 4.3

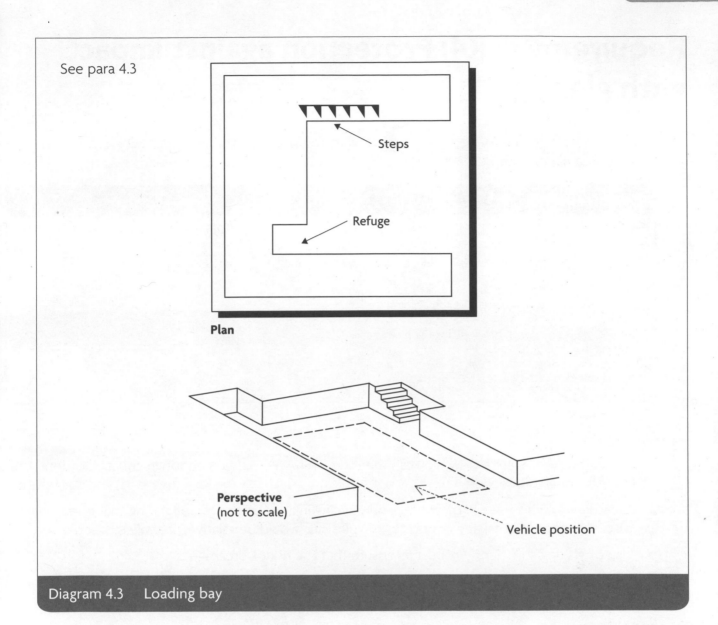

Plan

Perspective
(not to scale)

Vehicle position

Diagram 4.3   Loading bay

Requirement K4: Protection against impact with glazing

This approved document deals with the following requirement from Part K of Schedule 1 to the Building Regulations 2010.

Requirements	
Requirement	*Limits on application*
Protection against impact with glazing	
K4.—Glazing, with which people are likely to come into contact whilst moving in or about the building shall:	
(a) if broken on impact, break in a way which is unlikely to cause injury; or	
(b) resist impact without breaking; or	
(c) be shielded or protected from impact.	

Performance

In the Secretary of State's view, you can meet requirement K4 if you adopt, in critical locations, one of the following approaches.

a. Measures to limit the risk of cutting and piercing injuries by the use of glazing that is reasonably safe, such that, if breakage did occur, any particles would be relatively harmless.

b. Use of glazing sufficiently robust to ensure that the risk of breakage is low.

c. Steps are taken to limit the risk of contact with the glazing.

Impacts with glazing, particularly glazing in doors and door side panels, and at low level in walls and partitions, can result in cutting and piercing injuries. For doors and door side panels, the risk is greatest for glazing between floor and shoulder level when near to door handles and push plates, especially when normal building movement causes doors to stick.

Hands, wrists and arms are particularly vulnerable. An initial impact at between waist and shoulder levels can be followed by a fall through the glazing, resulting in additional injury to the face and body.

In walls and partitions, away from doors, the risks relate predominantly to glazing at low level. At that level, children are especially vulnerable.

Section 5: Protection against impact with glazing

Glazing in critical locations

For all buildings

5.1 Diagram 5.1 shows critical locations in terms of safety.

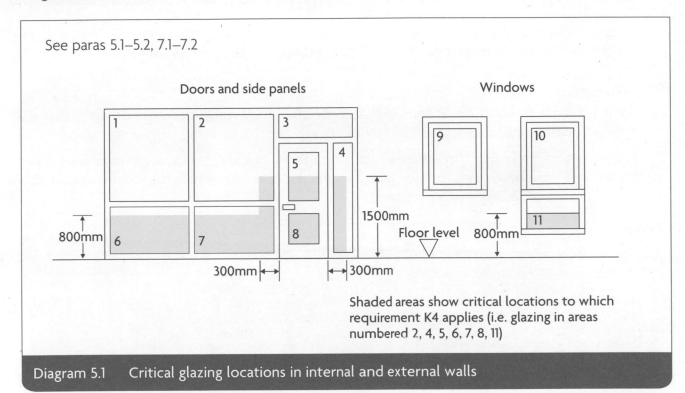

See paras 5.1–5.2, 7.1–7.2

Doors and side panels

Windows

1500mm

Floor level

800mm

800mm

300mm

300mm

Shaded areas show critical locations to which requirement K4 applies (i.e. glazing in areas numbered 2, 4, 5, 6, 7, 8, 11)

Diagram 5.1   Critical glazing locations in internal and external walls

5.2 In critical locations, comply with one of the following.

a. Ensure that glazing, if it breaks, will break safely (see paragraphs 5.3 and 5.4).

b. Choose glazing that is one of the following:

(i)   robust (see paragraph 5.5)

(ii)   in small panes (see paragraphs 5.6 and 5.7).

c. Permanently protect glazing (see paragraph 5.8).

Safe breakage

5.3 Safe breakage is defined in **BS EN 12600** section 4 and **BS 6206** clause 5.3. In an impact test, a breakage is safe if it creates one of the following.

   a. A small clear opening only, with detached particles no larger than the specified maximum size.

   b. Disintegration, with small detached particles.

   c. Broken glazing in separate pieces that are not sharp or pointed.

5.4 A glazing material would be suitable for a critical location if it complies with one of the following.

   a. It satisfies the requirements of Class 3 of **BS EN 12600** or Class C of **BS 6206**.

   b. It is installed in a door or in a door side panel and has a pane width exceeding 900mm and it satisfies the requirements of Class 2 of **BS EN 12600** or Class B of **BS 6206**.

Robustness

5.5 Some glazing materials such as annealed glass gain strength through thickness; others such as polycarbonates or glass blocks are inherently strong.

The maximum dimensions for annealed glass of different thicknesses for use in large areas forming fronts to shops, showrooms, offices, factories and public buildings with four edges supported are shown in Diagram 5.2 (see also paragraph 7.1).

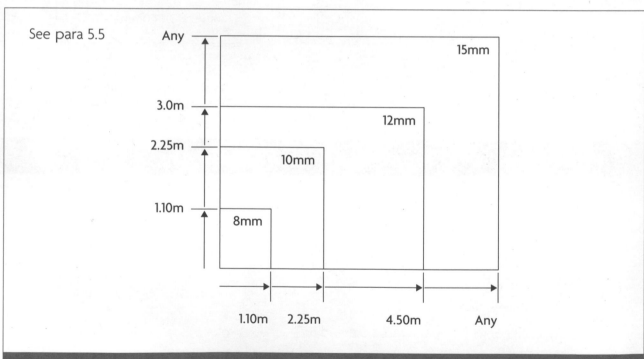

Diagram 5.2   Annealed glass thickness and dimension limits

Glazing in small panes

5.6 In the context of this approved document, a 'small pane' is an isolated pane or one of a number of panes held in glazing bars, traditional leaded lights or copper lights (see Diagram 5.3).

5.7 Small panes should be provided in accordance with all of the following.

a. In a small annealed glass pane, use glass with a minimum 6mm nominal thickness *except in the situation described in b.*

b. In traditional leaded or copper lights, when fire resistance is not important, you may use 4mm glass.

c. Use the dimensions and areas shown in Diagram 5.3.

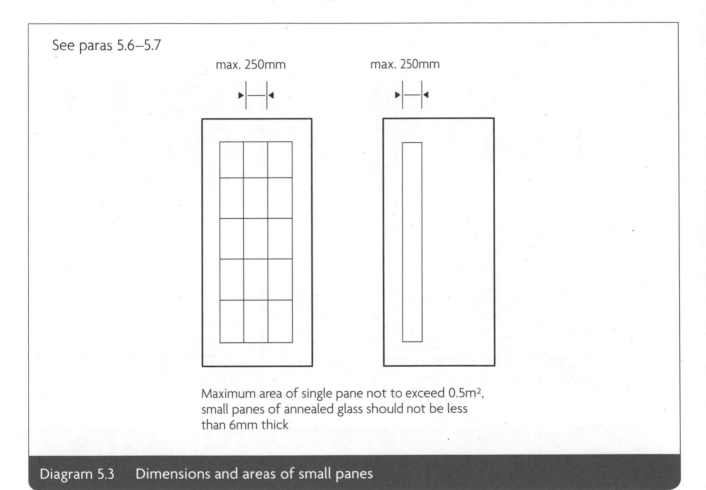

See paras 5.6–5.7

max. 250mm   max. 250mm

Maximum area of single pane not to exceed 0.5m², small panes of annealed glass should not be less than 6mm thick

Diagram 5.3   Dimensions and areas of small panes

K4   Protection against impact with glazing

Permanent screen protection

5.8 If glazing in a critical location is protected by a permanent screen then the glazing itself does not need to comply with requirement K4.

The permanent screen should comply with all of the following.

a. Prevent a sphere of 75mm from coming into contact with the glazing.

b. Be robust.

c. If it protects glazing installed to help prevent people from falling, be difficult to climb (e.g. no horizontal rails).

See Diagram 5.4.

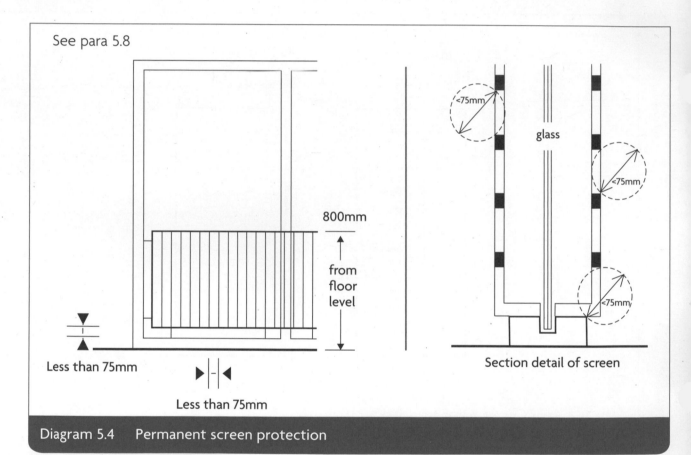

Diagram 5.4   Permanent screen protection

Requirement K5.1: Protection from collision with open windows etc.

This approved document deals with the following requirement from Part K of Schedule 1 to the Building Regulations 2010.

Requirements	
Requirement	*Limits on application*
Protection from collision with open windows etc.	
K5.1—Provision shall be made to prevent people moving in or about the building from colliding with open windows, skylights or ventilators.	Requirement K5.1 does not apply to dwellings.

Performance

In the Secretary of State's view, you can meet requirement K5.1 if windows, skylights and ventilators can be left open without danger of people colliding with them. You can achieve this by one of the following methods.

a. Install windows, skylights and ventilators so that projecting parts cannot come into contact with people moving in and around the building.

b. Install features which guide people moving in or around the building away from any open window, skylight or ventilator.

In special cases, such as in spaces where access is required only for maintenance, greater care can be expected from people and therefore a lower standard of provision may be acceptable.

Section 6: Protection from collision with open windows etc.

Projecting parts

6.1 Where parts of windows, skylights and ventilators project inside or outside a building, indicate this as shown in Diagram 6.1 or Diagram 6.2 (but see also paragraph 6.2).

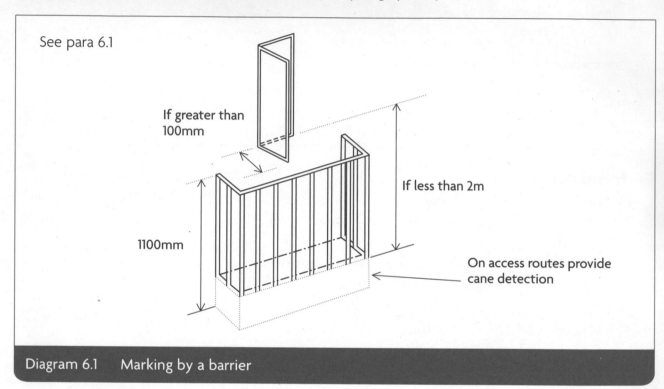

See para 6.1

If greater than 100mm

If less than 2m

1100mm

On access routes provide cane detection

Diagram 6.1   Marking by a barrier

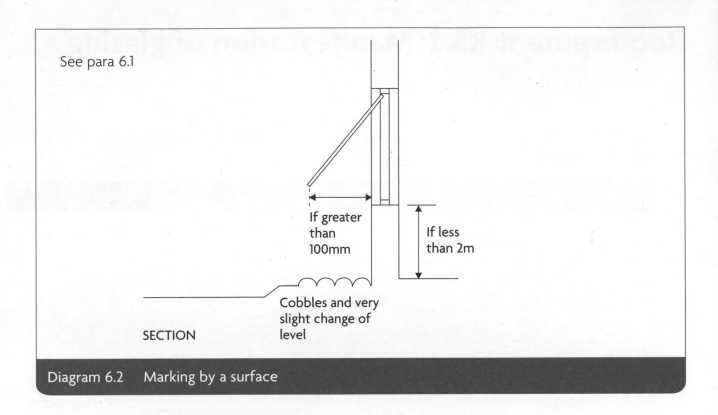

See para 6.1

If greater than 100mm

If less than 2m

Cobbles and very slight change of level

SECTION

Diagram 6.2   Marking by a surface

Spaces used only for maintenance

6.2 In spaces which are used infrequently and only for maintenance you can, for example, mark the projecting part clearly to make it easy to see.

Requirement K5.2: Manifestation of glazing

This approved document deals with the following requirement from Part K of Schedule 1 to the Building Regulations 2010.

Requirements

Requirement	Limits on application
Manifestation of glazing **K5.2**—Transparent glazing, with which people are likely to come into contact while moving in or about the building, shall incorporate features which make it apparent.	Requirement K5.2 does not apply to dwellings.

Performance

In the Secretary of State's view, you can meet requirement K5.2 by including, in critical locations, permanent means of indicating the presence of large uninterrupted areas of transparent glazing.

Section 7: Manifestation of glazing

Critical locations

7.1 Critical locations (see paragraph 5.1) include large uninterrupted areas of transparent glazing which form, or are part of, the internal or external walls and doors of shops, showrooms, offices, factories, public or other non-domestic buildings.

7.2 The risk of collision is greatest when two parts of the building, or the building and its immediate surroundings, are at the same level but separated by transparent glazing and people may think they can walk from one part to the other.

Permanent methods to indicate glazing, and alternative methods

7.3 People moving in or around a building might not see glazing in critical locations and can collide with it. To avoid this one of the following should be adopted.

    a. Use permanent manifestation to make glazing apparent (see paragraph 7.4).

    b. Use alternative indications of glazing, such as mullions, transoms, door framing or large pull or push handles (see Diagram 7.1).

7.4 Provide glass doors and glazed screens (including glazed screens alongside a corridor) with all of the following.

    a. Manifestation at two levels, as shown in Diagram 7.2.

    b. Manifestation that will contrast visually with the background seen through the glass, both from inside and outside, in all lighting conditions.

    c. Manifestation in the form of a logo or sign, a minimum of 150mm high (repeated if on a glazed screen), or a decorative feature such as broken lines or continuous bands, a minimum of 50mm high.

    d. Where glazed doors are beside or part of a glazed screen, they are clearly marked with a high-contrast strip at the top and on both sides.

    e. Where glass doors may be held open, they are protected with guarding to prevent people colliding with the leading edge.

See para 7.3

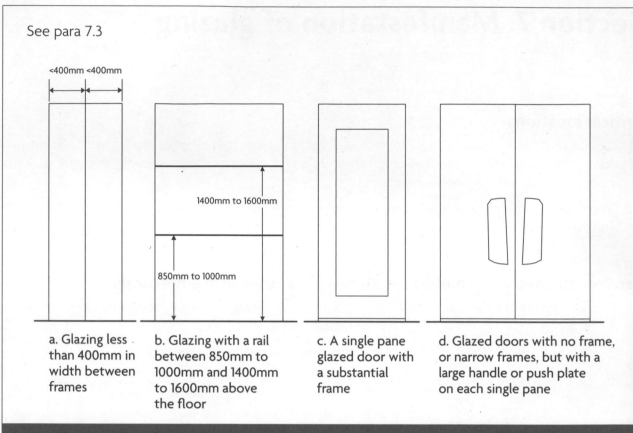

a. Glazing less than 400mm in width between frames

b. Glazing with a rail between 850mm to 1000mm and 1400mm to 1600mm above the floor

c. A single pane glazed door with a substantial frame

d. Glazed doors with no frame, or narrow frames, but with a large handle or push plate on each single pane

Diagram 7.1   Examples of door-height glazing not warranting manifestation

See para 7.4

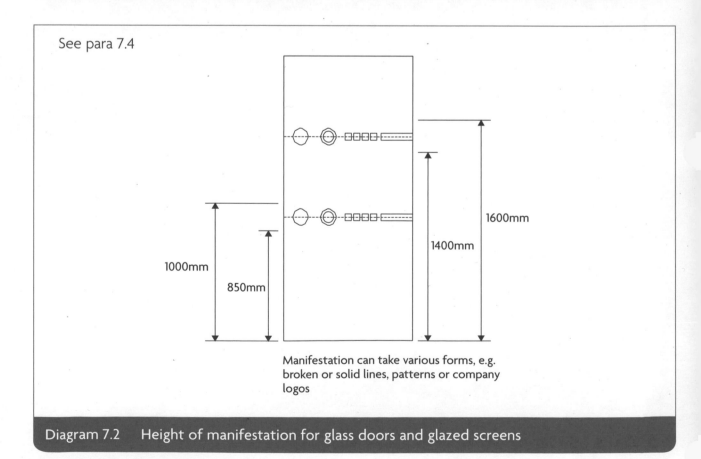

Manifestation can take various forms, e.g. broken or solid lines, patterns or company logos

Diagram 7.2   Height of manifestation for glass doors and glazed screens

Requirement K5.3: Safe opening and closing of windows etc.

This approved document deals with the following requirement from Part K of Schedule 1 to the Building Regulations 2010.

Requirements	
Requirement	*Limits on application*
Safe opening and closing of windows etc. **K5.3**—Windows, skylights and ventilators which can be opened by people in or about the building shall be so constructed or equipped that they may be opened, closed or adjusted safely.	Requirement K5.3 does not apply to dwellings.

Performance

In the Secretary of State's view, you can meet requirement K5.3 by ensuring that people can safely operate windows, skylights and ventilators that open.

Section 8: Safe opening and closing of windows etc.

Location of controls

8.1 Regarding the controls to operate windows, skylights and ventilators, one of the following should be provided.

a. Controls positioned as shown in Diagram 8.1.

b. If controls cannot be positioned as shown in Diagram 8.1 within safe reach of a permanent stable surface, provide a safe manual or electrical means of remote operation.

NOTE: Additional guidance is provided in Approved Document M for switches and controls and for window controls in sleeping accommodation.

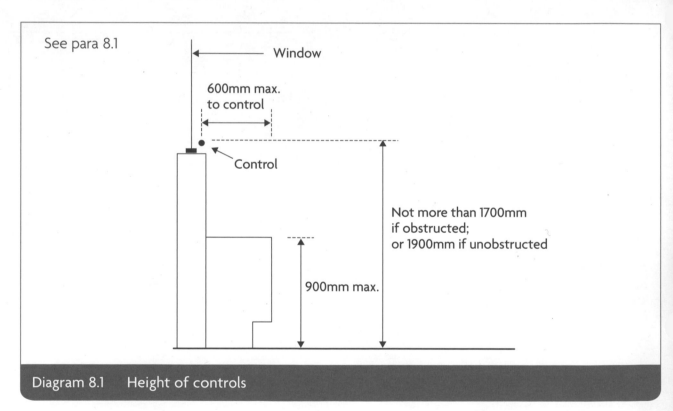

See para 8.1

Window

600mm max. to control

Control

Not more than 1700mm if obstructed; or 1900mm if unobstructed

900mm max.

Diagram 8.1   Height of controls

Prevention of falls

8.2 Where a person may fall through a window above ground floor level, provide suitable opening limiters, to restrain the window sufficiently to prevent such falls, or guarding (see Section 3).

Requirement K5.4: Safe access for cleaning windows etc.

This approved document deals with the following requirement from Part K of Schedule 1 to the Building Regulations 2010.

Requirements

Requirement	Limits on application
Safe access for cleaning windows etc. **K5.4**—Provision shall be made for any windows, skylights, or any transparent or translucent walls, ceilings or roofs to be safely accessible for cleaning.	Requirement K5.4 does not apply to: (a) dwellings, or (b) any transparent or translucent elements whose surfaces are not intended to be cleaned.

Performance

In the Secretary of State's view, you can meet requirement K5.4 if, where a person may fall from a window, you provide safe means of access for cleaning both sides of the glass.

Section 9: Safe access for cleaning windows etc.

Safe access methods

9.1 Where a person standing on the ground, a floor or other permanent stable surface cannot safely clean a glazed surface use one of the following methods.

   a. Provide windows of a size and design that allows people to clean the outside safely from inside the building (see Diagram 9.1). If windows reverse for cleaning, fit a mechanism to hold the window in the reversed position. For additional guidance, see **BS 8213-1**.

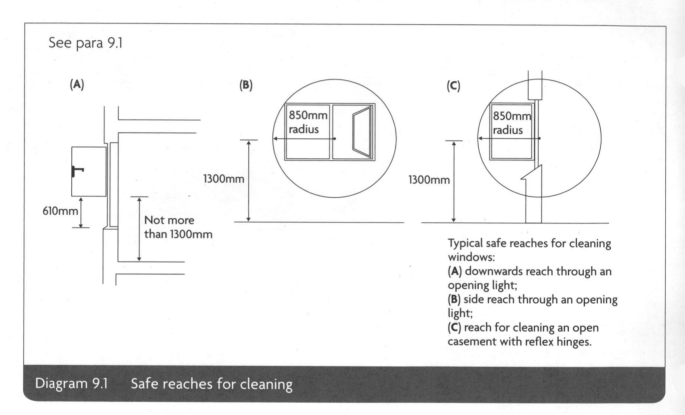

See para 9.1

(A)

(B)

(C)

610mm

Not more than 1300mm

850mm radius

1300mm

850mm radius

1300mm

Typical safe reaches for cleaning windows:
(A) downwards reach through an opening light;
(B) side reach through an opening light;
(C) reach for cleaning an open casement with reflex hinges.

Diagram 9.1   Safe reaches for cleaning

   b. Provide access ladders as follows:

      (i)   for ladders up to 6m long: as shown in Diagram 9.2

      (ii)   for ladders between 6m and 9m long: with safety features, as shown in Diagram 9.3.

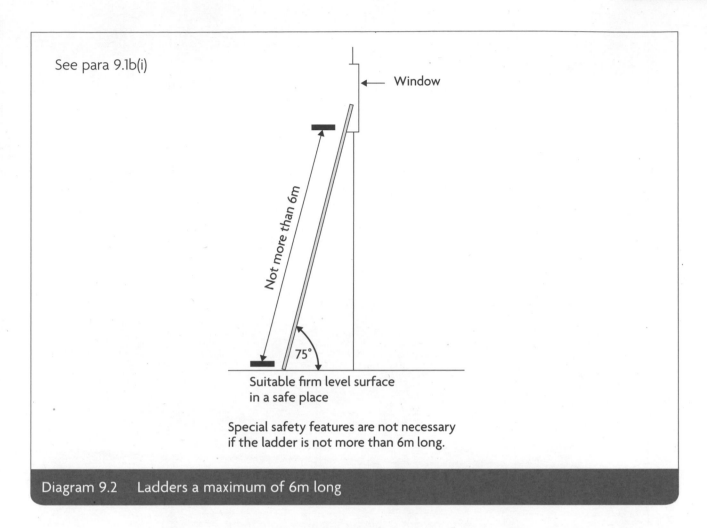

See para 9.1b(i)

Window

Not more than 6m

75°

Suitable firm level surface
in a safe place

Special safety features are not necessary
if the ladder is not more than 6m long.

Diagram 9.2   Ladders a maximum of 6m long

c. Provide access equipment such as suspended cradles or travelling ladders, with attachments for safety harnesses (see Diagram 9.3).

d. Provide suitable anchorage points for safety harnesses (see Diagram 9.3) or abseiling hooks.

e. Provide walkways at least 400mm wide, either with guarding at least 1100mm high, or with anchorages for sliding safety harnesses (see Diagram 9.3).

f. If the methods described in (a) to (e) are not possible, provide space for scaffold towers from which glazed surfaces can be cleaned.

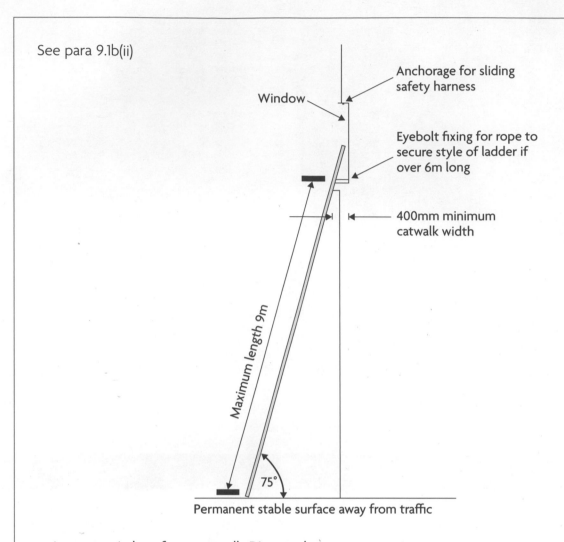

See para 9.1b(ii)

Window

Anchorage for sliding safety harness

Eyebolt fixing for rope to secure style of ladder if over 6m long

400mm minimum catwalk width

Maximum length 9m

75°

Permanent stable surface away from traffic

Access to windows from a catwalk. Diagram shows:
– fixing for ladder required if it is over 6m long
– anchorage for sliding safety harness (see 9.1e) for working on a catwalk

Diagram 9.3   Ladders a maximum of 9m long

Requirement K6: Protection against impact from and trapping by doors

This approved document deals with the following requirement from Part K of Schedule 1 to the Building Regulations 2010.

Requirements

Requirement	Limits on application

Protection against impact from and trapping by doors
 	
K6.—(1) Provision shall be made to prevent any door or gate:
    (a) which slides or opens upwards, from falling onto any person; and
    (b) which is powered, from trapping any person.
 	
(2) Provision shall be made for powered doors and gates to be opened in the event of a power failure.
 	
(3) Provision shall be made to ensure a clear view of the space on either side of a swing door or gate.
	Requirement K6 does not apply to:
	
	(a) dwellings, or
	(b) any door or gate which is part of a lift.

Performance

In the Secretary of State's view, you can meet requirement K6 if you take measures to prevent the opening and closing of doors and gates presenting a safety hazard.

Section 10: Protection against impact from and trapping by doors

Safety features

10.1 Doors and gates should be constructed in accordance with all of the following.

a. In door leaves and side panels wider than 450mm, include vision panels towards the leading edge of the door to provide, as a minimum, the zone or zones of visibility shown in Diagram 10.1.

b. For sliding doors and gates, provide both of the following:

    (i) a stop or other effective means to prevent them coming off the end of the track

    (ii) a retaining rail to prevent doors and gates falling if the suspension system fails or the rollers leave the track.

c. On upward-opening doors and gates, fit a device to stop them falling in a way that may cause injury.

d. For power-operated doors and gates, provide all of the following:

    (i) safety features (such as a pressure-sensitive door edge which operates the power switch) to prevent injury to people who are struck or trapped

    (ii) a readily identifiable and accessible stop switch

    (iii) the ability for manual or automatic opening if there is a power failure, when necessary for health or safety.

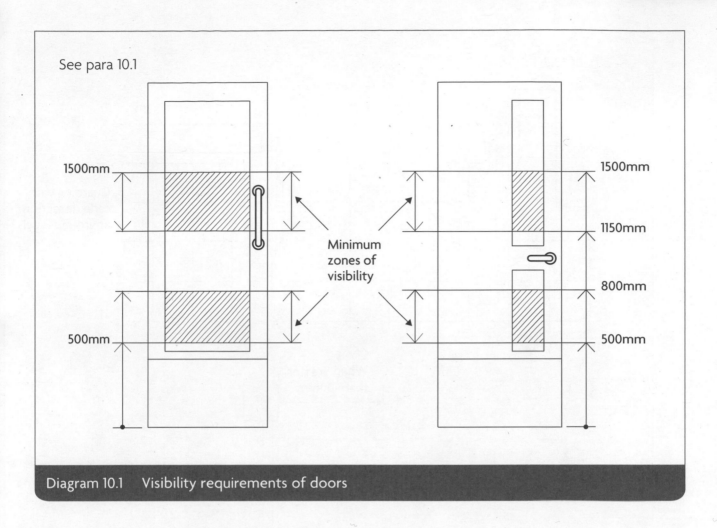

Diagram 10.1   Visibility requirements of doors

Hazards on access routes

10.2 If, during normal use, doors (excluding fire escape doors) swing out by more than 100mm towards an access route, protect them as shown in Diagram 10.2.

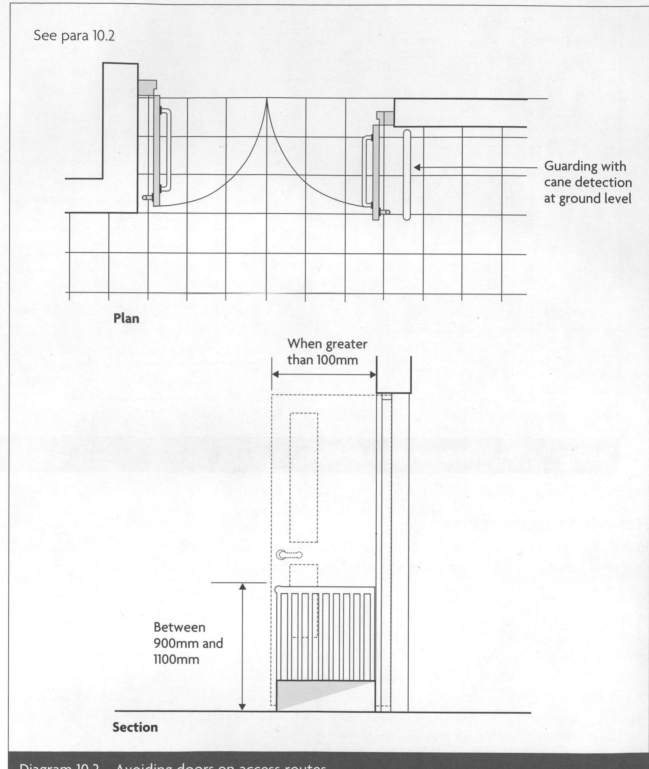

See para 10.2

Plan

Guarding with cane detection at ground level

When greater than 100mm

Between 900mm and 1100mm

Section

Diagram 10.2   Avoiding doors on access routes

Appendix A: Key terms

The following are key terms used in this document:

Accessible entrance
An entrance which is accessible to people regardless of disability, age or gender.

Alternating tread stair
A stair with paddle-shaped treads where the wide portion is on alternate sides on consecutive treads (see paragraphs 1.29 and 1.30).

Barrier
A structure – either a raised rail or a solid wall – that denies access to another area.

Common stair
Serving more than one dwelling.

Contrast visually
The perception of a visual difference between two elements of the building, or fittings within the building, so that the difference in light reflectance value is of sufficient points to distinguish between the two elements.

Flight
A continuous series of steps or a continuous slope (ramp) between landings. (For the widths and lengths of flights see paragraphs 1.14–1.24.)

General access stair
A stair intended for all users of a building on a day-to-day basis, as a normal route between levels.

Going
For stairs: the depth from front to back of a tread, less any overlap with the next tread above (see paragraphs 1.2 and 1.3). (For the measurement of the going on tapered treads see paragraphs 1.25–1.27.)

For ramps: the length of the ramp between landings.

Guarding
A barrier that denies pedestrians or vehicles access to another area, for example the floor below (see Diagrams 3.1 and 3.2).

Handrail
A rail, at hand height or a little higher, for people to hold for support. (For handrails for stairs, see paragraphs 1.34–1.37; for handrails for ramps, see paragraphs 2.11–2.12.)

Helical stair
A stair in a helix around a central void (see paragraph 1.28).

Ladder
A means of access to another level, formed by a series of rungs or narrow treads. People normally ascend or descend facing the ladder. (See paragraphs 1.31–1.33.)

Light reflectance value (LRV)
The total quantity of visible light reflected by a surface at all wavelengths and directions when illuminated by a light source.

Nosing
The leading edge of a stair tread.

Pitch
The angle of inclination (slope) between the horizontal and a line connecting the nosings of a stair.

Private stair
A stair intended to be used for only one dwelling.

Principal entrance
An entrance which a visitor not familiar with the building would normally expect to approach.

Radial gangway
A gangway at an angle to the rows of seats/wheelchair spaces or a stepped gangway in tiered seating.

Ramp
A slope steeper than 1:20, on which a pedestrian or wheelchair user can move from one level to another (see Section 2).

Rise
The height between consecutive treads (see paragraphs 1.2 and 1.3).

> For ramps: the vertical distance between each end of the ramp flight.

Spiral stair
A stair in a helix around a central column (see paragraph 1.28).

Stair width
The clear width between the walls or balustrades.

Tapered tread
A step in which the going reduces from one side to the other (see paragraphs 1.25–1.27).

Transverse gangway
A flat gangway parallel to the rows of seating/wheelchair spaces.

Utility stair
A stair used for escape, access for maintenance, or purposes other than as the usual route for moving between levels on a day-to-day basis.

Vomitory exits
Storey exits provided within the body of a seating layout.

Appendix B: Standards referred to

BS EN 1991-1-1
Eurocode 1. Actions on structures. General actions. Densities, self-weight, imposed loads for buildings [2002]

National Annex to **BS EN 1991-1-1**
UK National Annex to Eurocode 1. Actions on structures. General actions. Densities, self-weight, imposed loads for buildings [2002]

BS 4211
Specification for permanently fixed ladders [2005 + AMD A1, Corrigenda C1, C2]

BS 5395-2
Code of practice for the design of helical and spiral stairs [1984 + AMD 6076, Corrigenda July 2008, C2, C3]

BS 5395-3
Code of practice for the design of industrial type stairs, permanent ladders and walkways [1985 + AMD 14247]

BS 6180
Barriers in and about buildings. Code of practice [2011]

BS 6206
Specification for impact performance requirements for flat safety glass and safety plastics for use in buildings [1981 + AMDs 4580, 5189, 7589, 8156, 8693]

PD 6688-1-1
Recommendations for the design of structures to BS EN 1991-1-1 [2011]

BS 8213-1
Windows doors and rooflights. Design for safety in use and during cleaning of windows, including door-height windows and roof windows. Code of practice [2004]

BS EN 12600
Glass in building – Pendulum test – Impact test method and classification for flat glass [2002 + incorporating corrigendum April 2010]

Index

V

W